CORNWAL

MINING INDU

- A BRIEF HISTORY -

ALLEN BUCKLEY

TOR MARK

Published by Tor Mark,
United Downs Industrial Estate,
Redruth, Cornwall TR16 5HY

www.tormark.co.uk

First published 2002, reprinted 2008
This third edition 2020

ISBN 9780 85025 467 9

Printed and bound in the UK

COVER: (BACK) 420FM LEVEL ROSKEAR B 1130W
SHRINK STOPE 1994. (FRONT) BILLY DEVLIN
SHINKAGE STOPING – ROSKEAR D LODE ABOVE
THE 420FM LEVEL AT SOUTH CROFTY MINE.
TITLE PAGE: LARGE STOPED AREA OF GREAT
LODE WHEAL AGAR. THIS WAS WORKED BY HAND
LABOUR IN LATE 19TH CENTURY.

EARLY HISTORY

Over the centuries Cornish miners have discovered and exploited many valuable metallic minerals; tin, copper, wolfram, arsenic, zinc, lead, silver, colbalt and uranium. The industry can be traced back to the Early Bronze Age (2100 – 1500 BC). Archaeological and written evidence have made it the most interesting of ancient British Industries. This long history has been marked by significant achievements and has involved courage, perseverance, innovation, and ingenious invention. All this has generated a story of abiding interest for 21st century people throughout the world. Men and women of all ages and social groups have been fascinated by the history of mining in Cornwall.

Over the last two centuries a great many artifacts have been found on ancient tin sites throughout Cornwall, which have been identified by archaeologists as from the Early, Middle and Late Bronze Ages. Iron Age and Roman period finds have also been discovered and verified. Finds in all the main tin-producing localities between Dartmoor and Land's End show that from as early as 1500 BC the extraction of tin has probably continued without serious interruption until the present day.

Evidence of a well- established and sophisticated tin trade between Cornwall and the Mediterranean from as early as the 4th century BC is supported by written historical sources. There is scant evidence that any of the great events of history did any more than temporarily disturb that international trade.

BELOW:
LARGE SLOPE IN NEW COOK'S KITCHEN MINE. WORKINGS DATE FROM 17TH CENTURY.

Timaeus of Sicily and Pytheas of Massalia (Marseilles), of the 4th and 3rd centuries BC, gave accounts of Cornwall's tin trade. Neither author's work has survived but from fragments quoted by other authors it is clear that Pytheas had visited and probably circumnavigated

Britain some time between 325-250BC. In the 1st century BC Diodorus Siculus quoted Pytheas' report and told much about the nature and importance of Cornwall's tin trade. He said the Cornish were friendly and civilised, due to contact with foreign merchants. They extracted the tin from its host rock 'in an ingenious manner'. He refers to their skill in dressing and smelting the concentrate and then describes how they conveyed the metallic tin to an offshore island called Ictis. The island, generally presumed to be St Michael's Mount, could only be approached at low tide. The tin was then carried across to Gaul and then by horseback to the mouth of the Rhône, where modern day Marseilles is located. We are left in no doubt as to the importance of the trade.

From the earliest times to the end of the Medieval period most tin in Cornwall came from streaming alluvial deposits. Over thousands of years cassiterite was weathered from the outcrops of lodes, and washed by flood into the nearest valley. Beds of sand and gravel containing tin ore were laid down, with layers of barren material between and overlaying them. After removing the overburden, the tinners used water to wash away the lighter waste material. Several methods were employed, depending upon the slope and width of the valley as

BELOW:
WHEAL FRIENDLY.

well as the depth of the tin strata. Using sloping tye channels they first roughly washed the tin-bearing sand and gravel, before removing it to nearby dressing floors for buddling into black tin concentrate.

Even in ancient times every tin district had several 'blowing houses' where 'black tin' (tin oxide) was smelted into 'white tin' metal. It was usually smelted twice. Alluvial working continued at St Erth and Lanlivery into the twentieth century. Lode mining began in Cornwall at a very remote period but due to the large amount of alluvial tin available it was restricted to lodes exposed in cliffs or on rocky hillsides. It is possible that Diodorus' reference to 'earthy veins' in rocky ground is to lode working. Tin was certainly mined before the time of Christ in Spain and elsewhere.

By the late Middle Ages tin mining was widespread in Cornwall and as early as 1296 skilled Cornishmen were sent to work the royal silver mines at Combe Martin in Devon. By the middle of the 15th century, especially in Gwennap, Lanivet, Warleggan, Breage and St Just parishes, underground mining was replacing streaming in importance. This trend was accompanied by a westward shift in the centre of the industry, confirmed by production figures in Stannary records.

Many of those early mines were opencast trenchworks, which worked downward along the strike of the lode. Relistian, Mulberry ('Mulyera'), Wheal Whisper (Great Treveddoe) and Great Wheal Fortune ('An Coghan Bras') in Gwinear, Lanivet, Warleggan and Breage, are all examples of late Medieval opencast mines that were worked till modern times, and can still be seen. In the western Stannary districts of Penwith, Kerrier and Tywarnhaile, the opencast workings were called 'coffin' works. In the central and eastern stannaries of Blackmore and Foweymore, and in Devon, they were known as 'beam' works. Many of the early Tudor mine bound registrations were for these openworks. Richard Carew visited some in the 1580s, and said they were worked open to the sky to depths of 300ft. By Carew's time, however, most lode mines were of the shaft and level type.

Precisely when shaft and level mining began in Cornwall it is impossible to say. Undoubtedly some of the earliest cliff mines used levels supplied with shafts for ventilation, access and ore hoisting. As the lodes were pursued away from the cliff these would be necessary developments. It is apparent that the miners who went to Coombe Martin in 1296 were familiar with such methods, for the records show that Devon silver mines had adit levels and shafts. Iron poll picks, gads, plugs and feathers and chisels were all used to hew the rock.

Leather buckets hoisted water to the adit drainage level, and lighting was by tallow candle. In the 18th century it was believed that such mining methods were first used in the 1450s but recent research has pushed Cornish mining methods to a very early period. By the second half of the 15th century, references to speculative shafts being sunk over 70 feet at costs of up to £1.9s.0d. a foot, and employing scores of miners, show that shaft and level mining was well past its infancy. Tin bound registrations for the early Tudor period indicate some mines with a handful of workers and others employing hundreds.

16TH CENTURY INDUSTRY

Richard Carew and Thomas Beare have left clear and comprehensive descriptions of the tin industry In the late 16th century. They vividly describe mining in the Breage - Germoe area and tin streaming in the St Austell area. A company of adventurers was formed to work a mine. They took a lease or registered bounds, appointed a mine captain to manage the mine, and hired miners or worked themselves. An 'accompt day' was arranged, usually once a month, when ore was shared, bargains were made and costs were assessed and divided.

The mine captain organised all aspects of the mine. He assigned tasks, agreed bargains and ensured the mine was drained, ventilated, supported and safe. The miners' tools were:

A pickaxe [poll pick] of iron about sixteen inches long, sharpened at the one end to peck, and flat-headed at the other to drive certain little iron wedges wherewith they cleave the rocks. They also have a broad shovel, the utter part of iron, the middle of timber, into which the staff is slopewise fastened.

Carew described both types of lode mine, opencast and shaft and level. The latter was used, he said, when a lode dipped 'slopewise'.

The tinners dig a convenient depth and then pass forward underground so far as the air will yield them breathing, which, as it beginneth to fail, they sink a shaft down...to admit a renewing vent.

Problems of soft ground and support work were also described, as were the inherent dangers of mining. Carew marvelled at the skill of the mine captains in accurately surveying ('compassing') to bring the drainage adit home to the workings with precision. The mine captain also had to ensure that the ore was broken and raised at sufficiently high grade, and was then crushed and dressed efficiently, economically and without undue waste. The 16th century mine Carew described was often a large affair. Driving adits and other levels, opening up new ground, stoping the lodes, sinking winzes and shafts, supporting the workings, setting and operating the pumps, moving the ore underground and hoisting it to the surface, all took a numerous workforce.

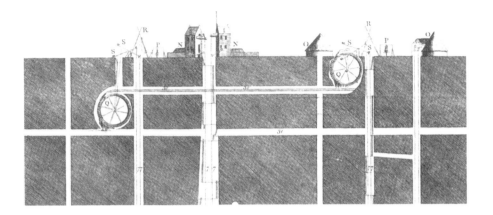

ABOVE:
THE TWO WATER
ENGINES AT BULLEN
GARDEN MINE FROM
WILLIAM PRYCE,
DRAWN IN THE LATE
1760S.

Similarly, the surface arrangements were labour-intensive. The machinery, in the shape of hoisting gear, pumps, waterwheels, sawmills, forge, carpenter's shop, stamping and crazing mills, as well as the numerous buddles and settling pits, would have occupied a large area with several permanent and temporary buildings. Godolphin Bal employed 300 workers in the 1580s.

When Carew visited the tin mines, overall production was in decline. A few large mines, together with several extensive 'bals' or groups of tin bounds, dominated the industry, though alluvial workings were still important. It is impossible to estimate accurately the number of tin producers at that time but registrations and other sources indicate they were spread throughout Cornwall. Having peaked in 1547, with the highest tin production for 150 years, the tonnage gradually dropped until after the Restoration (1660). In the 1580s the total annual tin metal produce from Cornwall was less than 600 tons.

Carew identified the main technical problem for tin mining by the end of the 16th century:

For conveying away the water they pray in aid of sundry devices, as adits, pumps, and wheels driven by a stream and interchangeably filling and emptying two buckets, with many such like, notwithstanding the springs so encroach upon these inventions as in sundry places they keep men and somewhere horses also, at work both day and night without ceasing.

Plunger, suction and rag-and-chain pumps were used, with men, horses and waterwheels supplying the power. These problems, brought about by deeper mining, had two effects. First, mining was rendered more expensive, requiring a greater outlay of capital. Second, necessity stimulated invention and enhanced skill. Miners and mining engineers strove to overcome these problems through improved technology and practice.

Thomas Beare has left a brilliant description of how the Industry worked on a personal level and describes the social conditions, the way of life, the wages, the settling of Industrial disputes and the humour of the tinners.

17TH CENTURY INDUSTRY

By the beginning of the 17th century Cornish miners had gained a reputation as experts in all aspects of mining and mineral dressing. Their self-confidence showed in the challenges made to German miners during the activity of the Mines Royal Company in the 1580s. When James I (VI of Scotland) wanted skilled miners to develop the Scottish silver mines, he bypassed the Germans at Keswick, and brought Cornishmen an extra 500 miles, because:

The miners of our Dutchie of Cornwall...are held to be the most experienced and most exercised in such woorks of all other our people.

Not only were skilled miners required, but also a mine captain, timbermen, blacksmiths, 'ruffbudlers' and other competent ore dressers.

During the early 1600s, Cornish mining engineers were prominent as advisors to the government and the Mines Royal, throughout the British Isles. Men such as Francis Godolphin and Hanniball Vivian taught mining, ventilation, drainage and hydraulic engineering to entrepreneurs such as Hugh Myddelton and Thomas Bushell, among the most successful silver mine operators in the country.

Water remained the major preoccupation of mining engineers during this period. It had closed the ancient Devon silver mines during the 1480s and the problem had worsened as mines became deeper. Italian and German academics and scientists as well as English and Cornish writers such us Norden and Carew all highlighted the problem.

Between 1580 and 1640 dozens of mine pump inventions were patented by German, English and Cornish engineers. Some, such as Vivian's in the 1630s, brought some improvement but for the most part gains rarely matched claims. It was 1674 before Samuel Moreland's new metal plunger pump, with improved stuffing box, produced a significant improvement. This was amid a welter of patents and claims. The mines had to wait until the end of the century before Marmaduke Hodgson and John Coster's improved waterwheel-powered pumps revolutionised mechanical drainage in Cornish mines.

An anonymous description of tin mining in 1671 shows that technically the industry had hardly progressed since Carew's time. Ground-breaking techniques had remained fairly static as had ideas on finding and developing new, productive tin ground, although there had been improvements to stamping and ore concentration. Costean pits or assay hatches continued to be the main means for locating lodes as they had been for centuries. Adits were still brought relatively short distances into or beneath the workings.

The 1671 writer explained how a mine was discovered and opened up. The assay hatch, if a lode was found, became an access shaft, from the bottom of which the lode was followed downwards by 'shambles', or large steps. Each step was about 6 or 7ft high, so that broken ore could easily be thrown up by 'shovelmen'. When the lode became payable, drifts or levels were driven on its course and these were about 3ft wide by 7ft high. Levels were usually every 5 fathoms (30ft), leaving a convenient block of ground for stoping. When the levels were below adit the water was lifted to it by means of buckets, 'leathern bags' and pumps, which were either plunger, suction or rag-and-chain. A drift was advanced by three 'beelemen' ripping away the ore and deads whilst two 'shovelmen' removed it. They would barrow it back to the shamble, to be thrown up in stages

to surface, or to a shaft to be hoisted up with a 'winder with two keebles'. During the 1680s there was a dramatic change in mining practice. Shot-hole blasting with gunpowder, first successfully used in Hungary in 1627, arrived in Cornwall via Germany and the North of England. By the early 1690s its use was widespread and in Cornish mines it was to change the whole approach to

ABOVE:
WATERWHEEL-POWERED DRY
STAMPS, ILLUSTRATED BY
AGRICOLA IN 1556, ARE FIRST
MENTIONED IN CORNWALL IN
1493. ORE WAS WET-STAMPED BY
THE MID-SIXTEENTH CENTURY.

hard-rock mining. Adits longer than half a mile had previously taken a generation or more to bring home. Gun-powder meant that adventurers could plan schemes within the period of their lease that they could not have contemplated hitherto.

Figures for level advancement from that time show that there was a dramatic increase in daily footage achieved. Adit levels were frequently extended by over a foot a shift. One hundred years earlier, John Norden had written that it frequently took a week for levels to be driven that far. Stoping tonnages also increased considerably.

The late 17th century also saw advances in the financial organisation of mining companies. Articles of Association were drawn up and signed by all adventurers, and these covered every aspect of the enterprise. Working adventurers were being joined or replaced by outsiders, many of them farmers and merchants, and some from outside the county. Mining engineers, bankers and smelters were also prominent. The resultant financial stability made expensive long-term schemes, such as long adits or new pumping engines, more general. By the 1680s several of the important mines were well over 300ft deep, and moving into the copper zones of mineralisation, beneath the shallow tin.

COPPER MINING

We cannot be certain when the first copper was mined in Cornwall. Archaeology indicates that it may have been during the Bronze Age, perhaps over a thousand years before Christ, and it would be astonishing if the copper lodes clearly seen in the cliffs at St Just, Illogan, St Agnes and Perranzabuloe had been missed by the ancients. The Romans are known to have mined the metal in Wales, but there is no evidence of them doing so in Cornwall. Throughout the later Medieval period the English Crown granted licences to search for copper and other metals in many counties, including Cornwall, but it was not before the middle of the 16th century that much happened.

In 1555 a German mining engineer, Burchard Cranych, was given permission to search for copper in Cornwall. Early in Elizabeth's reign another German, Daniel Hochstetter, came to Cornwall to continue the search. He was part of the Mines Royal Company. They were not very successful. Twenty years later the Mines Royal were again involved, this time moving hundreds of Germans to Keswick, to mine, dress and smelt copper. They also brought a group of skilled miners to Cornwall under the direction of Ulrich Frosse. Under Frosse they re-opened Hochstetter's mines at Perranporth, Illogan, St Just and elsewhere, and made elaborate arrangements to drain the old workings and generate enough good grade ore to send to Neath in South Wales for smelting. Again the Germans were unsuccessful. Their technology was inadequate with regard to both mining and pumping. They laid the blame for failure on insufficient investment: the Cornish said they were inefficient and expensive. Frosse's letters display a lack of energy in his approach. By the early 17th century the Mines Royal had pulled out of Cornwall and was concentrating its capital on silver mining in west Wales. Ironically, as we have seen, it was to Cornish mining engineers that the Mines Royal turned for advice on running these mines.

It was during the period immediately prior to the Revolution of 1688 that copper again came to the attention of Cornish miners. As the mines deepened more copper was discovered. This was thrown aside as 'poder' or waste, unless it was particularly pure. This might have been the end of it had it not been for changing political, economic and industrial conditions in England.

The late 17th century was a period of intense activity throughout the country. Everywhere old industries were expanding, new industries were springing up, new inventions were coming into use and joint-stock capital was becoming available to fund it all. Advances in metal mining techniques were part of this pattern, as were major developments in mine pumping machinery. Impetus also came from parliamentary legislation which removed the Crown's oppressive monopoly of metal mining.

Coinciding with these changes was the demise of Sweden as England's main supplier of copper – and copper was a central raw material in the successful expansion of industry, not just for itself but as the main constituent of brass and bronze. The zinc ore calamine, used in brass making, had been discovered in the Mendips in the 16th century, and now it was mined again for use in the burgeoning Bristol brass foundries.

By the early 1690s agents for the new copper smelting companies were visiting mines in several important tin mining parishes, and buying 'poder' very cheaply. John Coster, Gabriel Wayne, John Galethy and others purchased large tonnages of copper ore for transportation back to Bristol, where the new reverberatory furnaces were using coal to smelt the copper. With coal and calamine close to hand, and capitalists such as Sir Clement Clarke and Sir Ambrose Elton to back the projects, the success of the Cornish copper industry seemed assured. By 1700 these Bristol based industrialists appeared to have the whole thing in their control. Links were established with Midland manufacturers, ensuring them a steady and reliable supply of copper and brass. At the same time Coster and others took their plans a stage further by acquiring interests in the mines themselves. Their names began to appear on leases granted to companies of adventurers in those mines where most copper was being found. These Bristol-based businessmen became prominent shareholders in Wall Mine, Gwinear, in Pool Mine, Illogan, and in several other mines hitherto only concerned with tin. Within a few years the copper companies themselves took out leases on rich copper mines such as Chacewater Mine (Wheal Busy) and North Downs, Redruth, thus controlling every stage in copper's production. They were also prompted by the gradual rise of the South Wales smelters. The Mines Royal had maintained their Neath smelters since the 16th century, and in 1717 they were joined by Swansea. The Welsh had the advantage of proximity: they were a full day's sailing nearer to Cornish ports than their Gloucestershire rivals and eventually this proved decisive.

COPPER SMELTING IN CORNWALL

Almost from the start there had been attempts to smelt copper in Cornwall. The Mines Royal had smelted a little here in the 1580s. Before moving with their cash to Bristol in 1696, the Clarkes had been associated with two Cornish mines and other local businessmen in copper smelting at Polrudden near St Austell. This attempt lasted for four years and failed, it is said, due to bad management or dishonesty. Poor supply was the most likely reason. Little copper was raised in the St Austell area in the 1690s and agents scoured West Cornwall for ore without success. Due to the dominance of the Bristol smelters, Cornishmen continued their efforts to smelt copper themselves. In 1696 John Pollard of Redruth, together with local merchants, began smelting at St Ives. It was not a success due to lack of expertise, but they tried again in 1712 and continued successfully for a decade before closing. Pollard moved to Swansea, one of the first Cornish smelters to fight for independence outside the county.

Meanwhile in 1710, the year the government lifted duty on sea-borne coal to Cornwall, the Penpol copper smelter was set up, and this did very well, continuing successfully for 25 years. Undoubtedly the most successful smelting enterprise in Cornwall was that started by Sampson Swaine at Camborne in the 1740s. In 1748 he moved his operation to Dolcoath mine, one of the biggest copper producers in the county, and when coal supply became difficult he moved to Hayle, close to the harbour. The Cornish Copper Company was established at Copperhouse with several important Camborne mining families involved, including Trevenens, Johns and Vivians. They faced determined opposition from the South Wales companies and never matched them for tonnage smelted, but they survived well for sixty years before moving into tools and engine founding.

THE TICKETING SYSTEM

The crucial role which 'up-country' smelters and capitalists played in the initial stages of the Cornish copper industry, and which led to increasingly oppressive dominance by such outsiders, caused the establishment of a unique Cornish institution to combat it. The system of 'ticketing' for parcels of copper began in 1725: it involved piles ('parcels') of ore being sampled by the smelters' agents, who made bids in sealed envelopes for each parcel of ore. The ore went to the highest bidder. The advantages to the mine were that all ore was sold and the onus for assaying was on the buyer. These could become disadvantages once there was collusion between smelters. Later, neutral 'referee' assayers were used. The average grade of dressed copper ore was about 7 percent.

Although some ore was sold by private treaty, many lease agreements stated that all copper ore was to be sold by ticketing. With the demise of tin coinage in 1838, tin was also available for 'ticketing' and by 1890 most Cornish tin was sold by this system.

THE DOMINANCE OF COPPER

Historians have often judged the success of Cornish copper mining by its production and revenue figures. Using this yardstick the miners' attainments were truly impressive. From the 1680s, when a few tons of copper ore were sold to a couple of smelting companies, to the 1770s when the industry found itself in severe difficulty, a tremendous amount was achieved. In the 1720s 6000 tons of copper ore per annum, worth over £46,000, was shipped from Cornwall. This was about half the value of the tin raised at the time. By the 1740s production had risen to over 7500 tons a year, and revenue from copper was rivalling that from tin. By 1770 26,000 tons of copper ore was sold each year, realising almost £180,000.

Two facts put it all into perspective: Cornwall had become the biggest producer of copper in the world by a wide margin, and brass foundries in the Bristol district, new in 1700 and based firmly on Cornish copper, were the biggest producers of brass in the world by 1750.

During the 18th century copper mining altered the face of Cornwall. Great demographic changes occurred as workers moved into the mining parishes from 'up-country' and other parts of Cornwall. Camborne, Pool, St Day, Chacewater and other villages and hamlets became thriving centres of industry or towns. Insignificant tin mines or groups of tinbounds were transformed into large copper mines with hundreds working underground and hundreds more, including women and children, on the surface. The countryside was criss-crossed with water-carrying leats; waterwheels powering pumps and tin stamps occupied the valleys and hillsides in most mining parishes; on the larger mines great steam engines worked, their chimneys pouring coal smoke into the atmosphere; around every mine and in every hamlet the ancillary trades of blacksmith, ropemaker, cooper and candle-maker worked to supply the voracious appetite of the mines.

Alongside the ancient, almost timeless Stannary system which governed tinners, this new industry was extremely volatile. It was exciting, stimulating and always changing and expanding. New ideas, new inventions and new techniques were all part of this excitement. Cornwall became the centre of technological advance as inventors and engineers took up residence around the mines. Copper effectively made Cornwall the powerhouse of the English Industrial Revolution.

Fortunes were invested through joint-stock enterprise and even greater fortunes were generated. Water and steam power were improved immeasurably by the innovative activity of Cornish engineers and by English and Scottish engineers who were drawn here. Vast wealth was created by copper. The old landowning gentry advanced from agriculturally based comfort to great riches; merchants and bankers made fortunes; families such as the Williams and Lemons moved from humble backgrounds to unimaginable wealth and power. Intelligent and able miners became mine captains and mine managers in large numbers, as expansion increased opportunity. Everywhere the Cornish displayed enterprise and ingenuity unsurpassed anywhere in industrial history.

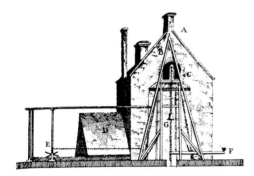

Fig.I.
South front of the Fire Engine.

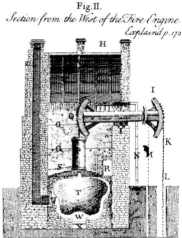

Fig.II.
Section from the West of the Fire Engine
Explained p.172

The Williams family of Gwennap and Scorrier rose from being humble tinners in Stithians at the end of the 17th century to become the agents for several local mine owners early in the 18th century. By mid-century they were seen as amongst the most energetic and knowledgeable of all mine managers, and

by 1800 they controlled or managed a quarter of all the copper mines in Cornwall, including some of the largest. A faster ascent was made by William Lemon. Born in Germoe into a poor mining family in the 1690s, he went from 'balboy', paid a few pence for watching the stamps, to control of one of the most important copper mines in Cornwall by his twenties. Before he was 50 he controlled copper mines in several of the richest parishes. He was known as 'the Great Mr Lemon', and before he died was without question the wealthiest individual in Cornwall: businessman, banker, landowner, mine owner and political manipulator. Like the earlier generations of Williams he never forgot his humble background. His grandson became a baronet and the family represented Cornwall in Parliament.

BAL MAIDENS

The period when women and girls were to play an important part in surface work on Cornish mines was during the years of the Copper boom between the beginning of the 18th century and the second half of the 19th century. The earliest extant, detailed copper mine accounts are from the 1720s and the 1730s, and these show that large numbers of bal maids were at work on the copper floors of Wheal Dudnance, Penhellick and Trevenson. There is no agreement of how many bal maidens worked on Cornish mines and tin streams. Figures from historians for 1787, 1799, 1836 and 1843 vary from between 1200 and 14400. There were 2500 bal maidens within 5 miles of Camborne at the time of the 1861 census. At their peak bal maidens made up between 15 and 20% of the mine work force.

Five basic tasks were carried out on the dressing 'floors' of copper mines : 'ragging', 'riddling', 'spalling', 'cobbing', and 'bucking', the last four of which fell to the bal maids. Ragging was carried out by youths using 14lbs (6.3kg) sledgehammers to break down the larger rocks. Next, girls of about 16 years would use a sieve-like apparatus to riddle or griddle the broken ore. The separated rocks were then beaten to fist-size by girls of a similar age using a spalling hammer weighing between 5 and 7 lb (2.3 and 3.2 kg). In the next stage girls of about 15 used a cobbing hammer to break away the ore from unwanted gangue material. This hammer had an unusual shape, having a long head which curved forwards rather than back, as with a pick. Finally the ore-bearing rock was subjected to bucking. The best-paid job, this was reserved for more experienced women, who could earn up to a shilling a day in the 1850s. A square-headed, flat-faced hammer was used by the bucker, who placed the gravel-sized rock on a metal plate or anvil. The bucker held her hammer with both hands, striking and grinding the gravel in one fairly deft movement. Other tasks of bal maidens were barrowing rocks across the dressing floors and general labouring. Descriptions of Cornish bal maidens by 19th-century essay writers and other visitors to Cornish mines have done their reputation no favour. Well-meaning middle-class do-gooders with liberal Ideas on working class behaviour have painted a distorted view of these proud, independent, self-confident and hard-working women. They were undoubtedly rough and ready, they were often outrageous in their behaviour - especially (as contemporary journals show) when copper agents were on the mine sampling - and some were foul-mouthed and loose in their morals. Maybe so, but such generalisations could be applied to almost any group during the Industrial Revolution. Many were also devout church and chapel goers. The bal maidens reputation for spending their hard-earned surplus cash on trifles, cheap clothes and visits to the fair is justified. It was their money, they had earned it and they spent it how they pleased. What is most important about these women is that they chose to be bal maidens even when better- paid and easier jobs were available. They were not, as some breast-beating modern historians insist, victims. They were not exploited. They chose a hard life on the mine - just as their menfolk under-ground chose theirs - because it was the kind of life they wanted. They enjoyed the singing, the banter, the camaraderie and the challenge. These tough, courageous, free-thinking women would have been insulted by those patronising historians whose view of the past owes more to the 'heart on their sleeve' than to the reality of how and why our ancestors did what they did.

THE GREAT COUNTY ADIT

A great enterprise in which both the Lemon and Williams families were involved was the County Adit. When William Lemon moved to Truro and became principal adventurer in several of the Gwennap mines, he became associated with John Williams, who ran them for several of the local gentry families. The most important of those mines was Poldice, famous for nearly two hundred years as a tin mine and by the 1740s becoming equally rich in copper. The combination of Lemon, already vastly wealthy and the finest business brain in Cornish mining, and Williams, the most dynamic and experienced of mine managers, was a partnership without equal. Poldice was unable to cope with unwanted water in her bottoms, 636ft from surface by the early 1730s. The duo attacked the problem with a two-pronged assault. Lemon used his great influence to lobby MPs to bring in an Act of Parliament to remit the duty on sea-borne coal, so that Newcomen's steam engines could be used economically, whilst Williams began planning the most ambitious drainage adit ever driven in Cornwall, 'Poldice Deep Adit'. The Act became law in 1741 and the Adit was begun in 1748. It started in the valley below Nanjiles and went north-west past Twelveheads to Haile Mills and then beneath Killicor Valley to the eastern end of Poldice Bal at Todpool. It was then driven right across Poldice to its western boundary by St Day.

This enormous undertaking was complete in about eighteen years and its cost was borne entirely by Lemon and his fellow adventurers. By the 1790s branches off the Adit went into Consols, United, and Wheals Fortune, Maid, Moyle, Quick, Jewell, Damsel, Hope, Unity and Unity Wood. A northern branch went through Creegbrawse to Chacewater Mine, and then across North Downs to Wheal Peevor, Cardrew and Treleigh. By the end of the century it drained over fifty mines in five parishes and was truly 'the Great County Adit'. It drained over 12 square miles and extended for 28 miles, the furthest point being at Cardrew, five and a half miles from its portal. By 1880 this vast network of drainage tunnels drained 16 square miles, had no less than 40 miles of adit and had served over 60 mines. Such was its importance

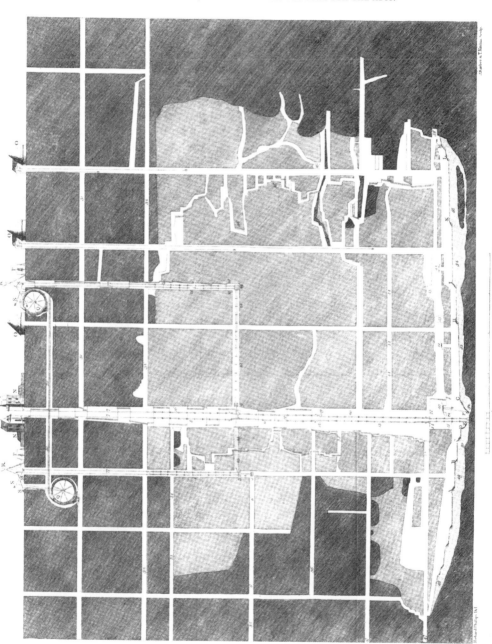

for the 160 years after its inception that few of even the largest and most profitable mines in the Gwennap area would have survived long without it. It was the most significant factor in the success of what was for many decades the richest mining district in the world. It became world famous as the supreme example of Cornish miners' grit and determination.

CORNISH COPPER MINING'S FIRST CHALLENGE

The thirty years after 1770 saw the Cornish copper industry face many problems. In 1768 a vast body of shallow copper ore had been discovered on Anglesey, North Wales. By that time Cornwall's copper mines had become too deep to work economically. Thomas Newcomen's atmospheric engines, the standard pumping engines for the large mines, had reached the limits of their ability. The great waterwheel-powered pumps, introduced early in the century by John Coster, were also reaching the limits of their capacity. These events, unhappily coinciding, almost ruined the Cornish copper mines. Judged on production figures alone we might conclude that the industry remained successful, for production continued to rise steadily during that period to a staggering 60,000 tons per annum. But with Anglesey ore profitably sold at £50 per ton and Cornwall's deep mines needing £80 a ton, it was no contest. For most of those years from 1770 to 1800 Anglesey and not Cornwall dominated world copper production.

Cornwall sought to fight the threat in two ways, by making its operation more economical, and gaining control of marketing through consolidation of mines and dictation of price. Remarkably, in the circumstances, it had a fair measure of success. Technical improvements, some through the inventive brain of James Watt and the business acumen of Matthew Boulton, achieved much but caused new problems. Consolidation and marketing activity also had some success and was eventually assisted by the exhaustion of Anglesey copper.

NEW MINING METHODS AND IMPROVED TECHNOLOGY

Understanding of the Cornish copper industry during the 18th century can not be made without appreciation of the technological advances of the time. In 1714 John Coster patented a highly efficient waterwheel-powered pumping engine. This rivalled for efficiency the atmospheric steam engine invented by Newcomen at about the same time. Until the last decades of the 18th century these two engines remained the only effective methods for mine pumping.

John Smeaton came to Cornwall mid-century and worked on the improvement of both waterwheel and atmospheric engine technology. He more than doubled the

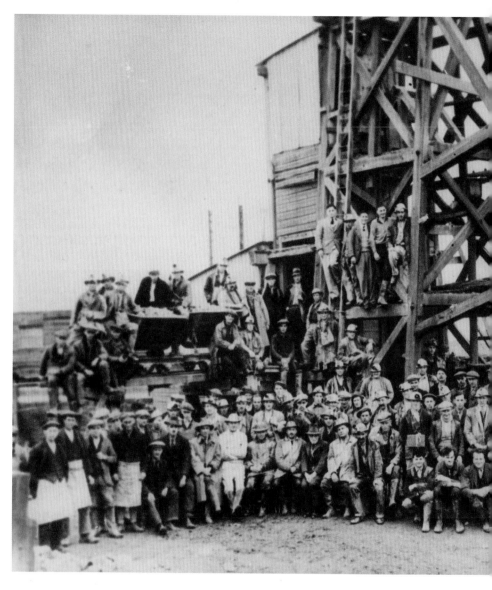

THE ENTIRE WORKFORCE
OF LADY GWENDOLINE
MINE, BREAGE IN 1937. THE
MINE CLOSED SHORTLY
AFTERWARDS.

efficiency of Newcomen's engine and made more effective use of water on Coster's. In the 1760s James Watt began introducing many improvements to steam power. He created the first true steam engine, with separate condenser, steam jacket and closed-top cylinder. He also patented a parallel rotation system that overcame the problem of transferring power to a horizontal beam from a vertical piston rod. Once again

efficiency and economy doubled. The political contacts of Watt's partner, the businessman Matthew Boulton, ensured that Watt's patent lasted until the end of the century. By that time Cornish and up-country inventors were champing at the bit. They were prevented from introducing modifications to improve existing steam engines, and the patent law was applied to prevent them inventing quite different engines.

In the last two decades of the 18th century several inappropriately named 'pirate' engines were tried on Cornish mines. The engineers Hornblower, Bull and Winwood all produced ingenious designs to circumvent Watt's patent. Inverted engines and compound engines were tried, at the same time that Richard Trevithick was experimenting with high-pressure steam. He was to create not only a high-pressure engine, but a revolutionary design for a high-pressure boiler. By the end of the century the engineers Lean, Murdoch and Trevithick had also increased pumping efficiency by re-introducing plunger pumps, to replace the suction pumps used throughout the 18th century.

The mines themselves changed totally during the first half of the 18th century. Working practices which are now regarded as 'traditional' Cornish mining methods were developed then. The tutwork and tribute systems, although not new, were refined to the forms that were to be exported to mining camps far from Cornwall. Tutworkers, or piece-workers, did most development on contract. Their bargains, which could be for one to three month periods, were bid for in a 'Dutch auction', the captain or manager regulating the price paid per fathom broken. The tribute system gave the miners a share of the ore broken and raised by them. High-grade ground might be priced by the manager at only a shilling in the pound, whereas a pitch in a poor stope might be offered at 18 or 19 shillings in the pound. Many mines tended to vary between 5 and 13 shillings.

There were many variations and exceptions to these basic rules. Some stopes were not 'set to tribute' but were given to stopers who were paid, like tutworkers, on the tonnage broken. Some tutworkers were paid on fathoms driven as well as a proportion of the value of ore broken and sent to surface. Some contracts included removal of ore to the shaft and some merely its breaking. Many miners, such as pitmen, kibble fillers and timbermen ('binders'), were paid from the 'company account', either monthly or by the day.

As the century progressed, and mines became deeper and more extensive, new and more efficient methods for every aspect of mining became necessary. At first the adit tunnel was the only true level in the mine. Work took place above or below adit. When deeper adits were driven under the older ones, mines acquired two main levels and these both became working levels. The system used in the 17th century of driving levels every five fathoms (30ft) was found inadequate, as larger tonnages of copper ore were being raised from wide lodes. Levels at ten fathom intervals became normal, although there was considerable variation from mine to mine. When it was no longer practical to hoist the ore to surface from a dozen points along a lode, due to depth, it became necessary to move the ore to central points underground. Fewer hoisting shafts meant better graded levels which became 'barrow roads'. Converting a level into a barrow road meant widening drives and cutting off corners to allow free movement. Frequently a groove was made along the centre of the level, or planks were laid to facilitate easy wheelbarrow movement. By design, levels ran downhill to central shafts, making ore movement and drainage easier. By the end of the 18th century some mines were probably using track of wood or iron for trams to run along, and this was a major improvement.

Throughout history Cornish mining methods have changed and improved. Groundbreaking techniques have been refined constantly, so that driving levels, sinking shafts and winzes, as well as stoping, have rarely remained the same for long. There is no doubt that stoping methods, the system used to remove the mineral lode from between the wall rock, have been developing from the 13th century onward. Even the earliest opencast and cliff workings probably used benches or steps to mine away the ore. Descriptions, sections and plans of mines from the 17th and 18th centuries show that a variety of methods was used to develop and stope the ground. Working downwards, in six or seven foot steps or benches ('stopes'), either to the next level or below the deepest level, is called 'underhand stoping'. Working upwards from the level with similar shaped benches is called 'back stoping', or 'stoping the back'. The earliest 18th century mine cost books show that both methods were well developed by 1710. Gunpowder shot-hole blasting lent itself to bench working in stopes.

At the beginning of the 18th century the deepest mines were around the 500 foot mark; by the end of it mines such as Dolcoath, Cooks Kitchen and Ale & Cakes were over 1000ft from surface and deepening rapidly. Poldice, the great tin mine in Gwennap, was 636ft deep by 1730 and would have been deeper if it had been able to cope with its water. By the end of the century many copper mines were far below Poldice and their workings were considerably more extensive. These copper mines quickly made the achievements of Godolphin Bal in the 16th century and Poldice in the 18th seem small beer, although those two tin mines had been legends in their own day for productivity, numbers employed and profit. A dozen early 18th century copper mines outstripped them in every particular. Chacewater Mine, Wheal Fortune (St Hilary), Longclose, Dolcoath and many others produced large tonnages and enormous profits during the early decades of the 18th century, and Pool Adit gave the Bassets £110,000 profit in the 1740s.

North Downs Consolidated produced in the period 1792-98 42,000 tons of copper ore, to the value of £353,000. Gwennap's United and Consols between them raised £797,000 worth of copper ore in 1792-1804, whereas Wheal Unity and Poldice produced no less than £800,000 worth, for a profit of £53,000 during the same twelve year period. Wheal Towan, in St Agnes, brought its principal shareholder, RADaniell, a 'guinea a minute' profit at the end of the 18th century.

A RESURGENT INDUSTRY
(OR THE 19TH CENTURY)

1800 represented much more than just the end of a century for Cornish mining. It marked the end of Cornwall's problems with Anglesey copper, the end of Watt's patent, the beginning of a period of amazing creative activity on the part of Cornwall's engineers and, although it was slow in getting under way, the start of the greatest and most productive period of Cornish mining ever. It also coincided with moves by Cornish mine owners to eradicate once and for all the dominance of outside smelters, be they Gloucestershire or Welsh. The great Cornish mining families took control of their own destinies during the early decades of the 19th century by moving their money into Welsh smelting, of which they retained control for much of the century.

In 1805 the price of copper rose to £138 a ton, the highest it had been, and moves immediately started to reopen mines closed during the 1790s. New discoveries unexploited during the decades of low prices meant that many new enterprises were also set on foot and several proved highly profitable. Cornwall again became the world's leading copper producer and remained so for several decades. This expansion, due largely to the continuing war with Napoleon, drew outsiders and their money into Cornwall. 'The Wise Men of the East', as the Cornish derisively called these outsiders, included one of exceptional ability. John Taylor had arrived in the West Country in 1796, when he took over Devon's Wheal Friendship and turned it into a model of efficient large-scale modern mining. Less than twenty years of age when he arrived, by his mid-30s he was moving westward into the traditional mining parishes of Cornwall and in 1819 he successfully negotiated leases for the great Consolidated mines. In 1824 he added United to his holding, creating at a stroke the single largest copper producing group in history.

Taylor is credited with introducing Cornish roller crushers into local mines in 1806, and with being among the first to use steam hoisting widely; the engines designed by his chief engineer Arthur Woolf were among the finest ever built. His success, however, is often exaggerated; mines such as United, profitable under the Williams before his time and after he relinquished it, always lost money for him. At times he matched the Williams for forward thinking and scientific planning but he never bettered them; so far as Cornwall was concerned, they remained throughout the 19th century the most successful mine operators.

Improvements to steam pumping engines, pitwork and boilers quickly followed the end of Watt's patent. It was not only the basic design of engines that improved during this period, but many peripheral modifications also greatly enhanced engine performance: the size and depth of the boiler furnace, better cleaning techniques and better lagging and insulation of cylinders. Engineers such as Jeffery & Gribble advertised their skill in improving

the performance of engines by watching them work and adjusting, modifying and altering the engine, boiler or pitwork. The service cost as little as £150. Remarkable savings in fuel costs were achieved, as well as great improvements in efficiency.

Arthur Woolf, William West, Richard Trevithick, Joel Lean and a host of other engineers were designing and testing engines of all sorts and sizes. As the century progressed the duty of these engines grew yearly. Duty of Cornish engines was measured in foot-pounds: how many pounds of water were lifted one foot by the use of one bushel of coal. However, a bushel is a measurement of volume, not of weight, which meant that the weight of a bushel of coal varied greatly. Eventually, coal was measured by hundredweight (cwt) and duty was expressed in millions. By this way of measuring, Newcomen's engines had given a duty of about 3.8 million by 1720, Smeaton's improvements increased it to nearly 8 million, Watt's original engines produced a duty of about 25 million and by the end of the 18th century duty was rising steadily. Thereafter the figures increased until by the 1840s engines were achieving duty of over 100 million and averaging 60 million. Then, for a variety of reasons, duty fell dramatically for the best engines, although the average declined at a gentler rate.

With the decline of Anglesey copper by 1800, the great Cornish copper families went on the offensive. They were still dominated by the smelters, now mostly centred around Swansea, and the Vivians, Williams, Foxes and Grenfells decided that if they could not beat the smelters they would join them – or take them over. Starting with Pascoe Grenfell in 1803, who helped set up The Copper Bank Smelting Works on the River Tawe at Swansea, Cornish money gradually took over firm after firm. By the 1830s the Williams, Daniell, Vivian and other Cornish families controlled a large part of the smelting industry and were well on the way to dominating it. Such was their strength that when, as the century progressed, foreign copper began to rival Cornish copper, these wealthy Cornishmen were able to retain their power and profit. Their amazing success during the first half of the 19th century is as impressive an example of initiative and enterprise as that of William Lemon and John Williams in the early 18th century.

The years down to 1838 saw many changes in the Stannary system which governed tin mining. What had seemed a traditional, easy-going and almost timeless regime found itself subject to and buckling under the irresistible pressure of modern economic factors. In 1837 copper also was placed under the stewards of the Stannary Courts but, with the abolition of tin coinage in 1838 and gradual reduction of all effective independence, the power of the Stannaries was coming to an end.

The decades that followed saw deep tin mining outstrip copper in many districts, and from the 1860s onward, tin not copper was the more modern, technically advanced and well organised industry.

THE MAN ENGINE

A device that has captured the imagination of those interested in Cornish mining history is the 'man engine'. For centuries Cornish miners climbed to and from their work places on ladders. As the mines got deeper the ladders became longer: by the 1830s several mines were past the 1300ft mark and sinking rapidly. As the mines got deeper they also got hotter and ventilation became worse. In some mines, especially Tresavean, United and Cooks Kitchen, extremely hot lodes were encountered at depth, so that temperatures in excess of 100°F were not uncommon. Older, experienced miners found it necessary to take less lucrative pitches at shallower levels, which meant financial loss to them and to the mine. Accidents in which exhausted men fell from ladders became quite common and the general health of miners deteriorated.

ABOVE:
A MARVELLOUS PHOTOGRAPH OF
DOLCOATH'S SINGLE-ROD MAN-
ENGINE IN 1893. THE
PHOTOGRAPHER, J C BURROW,
WAS STANDING INSIDE THE
STOPED-OUT LODE VOID, WHERE
THE SHAFT PILLAR SHOULD HAVE
BEEN: IT HAD BEEN REMOVED
FOR ITS RICH ORE CONTENT.

For humane as well as economic reasons mine owners and managers cast about for a remedy and some looked outside the country for ideas. In the 1830s German mines in the Harz Mountains had introduced a machine for lifting miners up shafts in stages. At first it consisted simply of large spikes driven into a pump rod at intervals corresponding to the height of the stroke. Small platforms were placed in the shaft, so that men moving upward stepped from the rod onto the platform and waited for it to return for the next upward stroke. This German 'man-engine', called a fahrkunst, was based on a 17th century Swedish machine that had been used for hoisting ore. The fahrkunst version developed into a double-rod engine, so that one rod rose as the other fell, and men stepped from one to the other as the rods paused after each stroke.

From the time of the first experiments in Germany the Royal Cornwall Polytechnic Society began to promote the introduction of something similar in Cornwall. Little was done at first, but within a few years adventurers in some of the deep, hot mines realised that with hundreds of their best men being forced to work in unprecedented heat, at hitherto unimagined depths, the survival of the mines as well as the men demanded that something be done. By 1840 miners were facing climbs up near-vertical ladders, many insecurely fixed, of well over 1500ft. It was, quite literally, killing them.

The RCPS offered a cash inducement to encourage mines to adopt schemes to alleviate the situation; in 1841, prompted partly by the Foxes of Falmouth, a humanitarian Quaker family, the engineer Michael Loam came up with a design. In January 1842 he installed his waterwheel-powered engine at Tresavean. It took men to and from the 24fm level without problems. Thereafter it was extended to the 248fm level, which was over 1700ft from surface, and was powered by a 36" steam engine. Loam's design followed the German fahrkunst and was a double-rod engine. In 1845 United Mines also installed a double-rod machine, powered by a 32" engine. Strangely, no more were erected until 1851, when Fowey Consols introduced a single-rod engine, powered by a 30ft waterwheel. Dolcoath, Levant and Wheal Vor all erected 'man engines' in the 1850s, but it was the next decade that saw the most activity, with no less than ten built between the Tamar (Devon Great Consols) and St Ives (Wheal Providence). Two more were built in the 1870s, at Crenvor & Abraham and South Caradon.

The Cornish were averse to the double-rod type of engine, seeing it as dangerous, so after the 1845 United engine all were of the single-rod type. Three man-engines were waterwheel-powered: the original Tresavean engine, Fowey Consols and Cooks Kitchen, which used an existing underground 52ft wheel, later replaced by a 26" horizontal engine. All the engines except Wheal Reeth (1861-69) were worked by cog-wheels, crank and flat rods. Wheal Reeth was unique in having the rod attached to the nose of the bob. The sizes of the steam engines varied from 19" up to 36", and averaged 26". The longest haul was made by Dolcoath's engine, which after several extensions and steam engine changes went 351fm down. It lifted men to surface at 83ft a minute and operated for over 40 years.

Many Cornish people remember Levant engine as it is always associated with the dreadful accident of 1919 in which 31 men were killed. Levant's man-engine served longest of all those erected in Cornwall. Built in 1856, extended and altered several times, with three changes of steam engine, the last being a compound 18-30", it finally collapsed in October 1919 after 63 years. Despite that accident, the second worst in Cornwall's mining history, the man-engine was probably the biggest boon for miners in deep mines during the 19th century. It saved hundreds of lives directly, and lengthened thousands by cutting out that murderous climb 'to grass' after an exhausting shift in mind-numbing heat.

CORNWALL'S MINERAL TRAMWAYS

A major problem faced by the mining industry was transportation. Movement of tin and copper ore to ports, and timber, coal and other supplies from those ports to the mines was fraught with difficulty and expense, for mule trains were the time-honoured method of moving all bulk cargoes. Expansion of copper mining in the second decade of the 18th century necessitated a drastic improvement. Tramways had been in use in some northern industrial areas from the 17th century and by the end of the 18th century it is probable that some Cornish mines had track and flange-wheeled wagons underground, although no progress had been made at surface.

Trevithick was among the first to appreciate what was required, but as usual his inventive brain was ahead of practical application. By 1801 he had demonstrated a workable locomotive and then displayed it in various parts of the country on track. Shortly thereafter Francis Basset, who owned some of the mines with which Trevithick was involved, promoted a plan to link his Camborne mines with his harbour at Portreath. Nothing came of the plan, but soon after, in 1809, work began to link Portreath harbour with the rich copper mines around Redruth. By 1812 the line went as far as North Downs, and was an immediate and highly profitable success. It was extended to Poldice by 1818 and was earning a fortune from the Gwennap copper mines, at that time the richest in the world. Some idea of the difference that this tramway made can be gauged by the fact that before its inception something in the order of 1000 mules a day carried copper ore into Portreath, each animal carrying between 2 and 3cwt. Once operating, the tramway carried most of the 25,000 tons of copper ore annually that went through Portreath in three-ton horse-drawn wagons. The success of the Gwennap-Portreath rail link may have influenced John Taylor's plans for a similar but more ambitious scheme to link Redruth and Chacewater to quays at Devoran. Taylor had gained the leases to United and Consolidated mines in Gwennap Parish, and was set to work them on an unprecedented scale. An Act of Parliament sanctioned the Redruth & Chasewater Railway and in 1825 work began to bring Taylor's plans to fruition. It very quickly eclipsed the Portreath-Poldice line in tonnage of freight carried to and from the mines. Taylor's mines became, during that time, the largest industrial complex in the world, employing over 3500 miners. His line carried a significant proportion of the world's copper ore, severely denting Portreath's trade.

The Redruth & Chasewater Railway was eventually 9½ miles long, including the branch to Wheals Buller and Basset. Some idea of its success can be gauged from freight figures. In the first 51 years of its operation the line carried 3.7 million tons of freight, including 1.7 million tons of copper ore and 1.5 million tons of coal. During that period the line made £104,000 profit and in only one year was there a slight loss. The wagons were horse-drawn between 1825 and 1855, after which two small steam locos were purchased. These were appropriately called Miner and Smelter and they were joined a couple of years later by a new engine called Spitfire. The line eventually closed in 1915, by which time the great Gwennap copper empire had itself been dead for over forty years.

In 1837 the foundations were laid for the Hayle Railway, between Hayle and Portreath; its original route was followed by the West Cornwall Railway, and later by GWR and British Rail. It linked the two most important ports on the north Cornish coast with the most important mining districts. Hayle and Camborne were also the principal engine building centres of Cornwall, containing Harvey's Foundry, The Cornish Copper Company, Holmans and Tuckingmill Foundry. Apart from the great steam engines these firms built, they also supplied tools and mining gear of every description to the mining districts of

ABOVE:
THIS TRAMWAY AT SOUTH CROFTY IN THE 1940S GIVES A GOOD IMPRESSION OF WHAT HORSE-DRAWN TRAMWAYS LOOKED LIKE. IT OPERATED FROM 1871 TO 1966, IN THE END USING DIESEL LOCOS.

the world. The line ran from Hayle and Copperhouse to Angarrack, and then along the present railway to the western side of Barncoose, where it turned north across Illogan Downs to Portreath. It ended with a spectacular incline, complete with steam-powered cable haulage. The line also went into Redruth and there was a long branch to Tresavean mine.

Much remains of those historical mineral railways, and industrial archaeologists regard them, as well as the scores of tramways confined to individual mines, as ideal routes by which to explore the unique mining landscape of west Cornwall.

CORNISH GUNPOWDER AND SAFETY FUZE MANUFACTURE

Since its introduction to Cornwall in the late 17th century 'black powder' as it was more often called had been imported from up-country at an extremely high price. Apart from the cost of its carriage from Somerset and other places of manufacture, the makers, conscious of Cornwall's need and their monopoly, added an extra premium. Some of them claimed, possibly spuriously, that it was the saltpetre that made it expensive.

By the beginning of the 19th century the Cornish decided to make black powder themselves, and in 1809 the first powder mill was set up in Cosawes Valley, by Ponsanooth. The setting was ideal, for thick woods covered a narrow, steep-sided valley which had an abundance of water. The buildings were easily dispersed in the trees, isolating them for safety. By mid-century such factories were producing powder throughout the mining districts and there was an immediate reduction in its cost to the mines.

There had always been an unacceptably large number of accidents from use of black powder. The Breage Burial Registers record the introduction of blasting there in June 1689 by Thomas Epsley and his death, possibly from blasting, in December 1689. In 1691 a Germoe miner called John Archer was killed at Trebollans Mine while 'shuting the rocks'. This name for shot-hole powder blasting persisted in Cornwall for over a century. As its use spread, such accidental deaths became common, and loss of sight, fingers and other serious injuries became daily occurrences in Cornwall. The methods of introducing the flame to the powder charge were primitive in the extreme, with 'rods' made from goose quills connected up and lined with bruised gunpowder being among the safest of 18th century fuzes. (The spelling 'fuse' was rarely used.) Such 'rods' frequently fired the charge prematurely, resulting in death or injury.

All this was to change with the invention by William Bickford in 1831 of the safety fuze. Bickford was a Devon man with a leather business in Tuckingmill, Camborne. He was horrified by the many deaths and injuries to miners due to blasting, and resolved to make it safer. He tried various designs, whereby parchment pouches containing a charge and a fuze were used, but without great success. Then one day he visited a fellow Methodist called Bray who operated a rope walk at Tolvaddon. As Bray walked backwards, spinning some yarns. Bickford had a brilliant idea. Why not pour gunpowder from a funnel into the centre of the rope as it spun?

Bickford, his son-in-law George Smith who was a carpenter, Thomas Davey, a miner with an aptitude for solving practical problems, and Bray, all of whom attended the same Tuckingmill Bible class, got together to produce a safety fuze that worked. This humane group of Methodists very quickly perfected a design that not only worked easily and safely, but was also simple to manufacture. The resultant 'safety rod' or safety fuze was patented in 1831 and after initial resistance became the standard blasting fuze in every mining region of the world. Tuckingmill, the village where it was invented, remained a centre of fuze production until 1961, when ICI, the last owners, closed the factory down.

As the 19th century progressed, both gunpowder mills and safety fuze factories were established in many mining parishes in the county. Large works at Kennall Vale, Ponsanooth, and smaller operations at Herodsfoot and Trago Mills produced black powder for local use, and fuze factories under several names competed with Bickford-Smith's factory at Tuckingmill.

ALTERED PRIORITIES IN THE SECOND HALF OF THE 19TH CENTURY

Judged by the sheer scale of activity and tonnage of mineral produced, Cornish mining undoubtedly peaked during the 1860s. At that time there were over 340 mines operating, of which almost 40% worked exclusively for tin, about 20% for copper, and a quarter produced a fair amount of both metals. Over a dozen mines produced lead; wolfram, arsenic, blende, mundic and silver were by-products of mines in several districts. Copper reached an annual average output of 181,470 tons of ore between 1855 and 1865. Tin metal from Cornish mines also peaked at over 10,000 tons in the years 1863-65; although it touched similar heights again briefly in the 1870s, tonnage fell inexorably thereafter. Over 40,000 workers toiled in those mines, with the majority (over 21,000) being employed in just 83 mines of between 100 and 800 employees. Although three great mines, Dolcoath, Devon Great Consols and

Clifford Amalgamated employed well over a thousand workers each, over 40% of Cornish mines had fewer than 70 workers, and 25% operated with less than 20.

Over 600 steam engines were working at that time. They varied from small whim and capstan engines, with a cylinder size of perhaps only 10" or 12" diameter, to great pumping engines of up to 90" diameter. These engines not only pumped vast volumes of water up shafts that were sometimes 2000ft deep, they also hoisted ore, and operated man-engines, crushers and stamps. The Cornish beam engine had been brought to perfection by the pupils of Trevithick and Woolf, and men such as James Sims, William West and Samuel Grose were designing and erecting engines that were to work efficiently and with economy for decades, in some cases until well into the 20th century. Over 220 mines had at least one steam engine, 44 had steam and water-powered engines, and a great many mines were operated exclusively by water power. In addition to this machinery, probably all the tin mines used some water-driven stamping engines. Some mines had enormous numbers of engines: Fowey Consols used 6 steam engines, 17 waterwheel engines and 3 hydraulic pressure pumping engines;

BELOW:
BLUE HILLS MINE, ST AGNES IN THE 1890'S. THIS WAS ONE OF THE LAST SMALL-SCALE MINING OPERATIONS IN CORNWALL. IT WORKED THROUGHOUT THE 19TH CENTURY BUT WAS NEVER VERY PROFITABLE. SCENES LIKE THIS HAD ONE BEEN COMMON IN MANY REMOTE DISTRICTS AND CORNISH MINERS WERE TO SET UP MANY MINING CAMPS LIKE THIS IN AUSTRALIA AND AMERICA.

Clifford Amalgamated had 11 steam pumping engines and numerous others for hoisting and crushing; Par Consols had 15 steam engines; and Devon Great Consols operated 7 steam engines and 32 waterwheel engines. Some tiny mines merely used small and extremely primitive 'flopjack' pumps to drain their workings.

It is as hard to generalise about Cornish mines during the mid-19th century as at any other period. Just as the numbers employed and the variety of machinery differed totally, so also did the mines themselves. In 1865 there were half a dozen mines that were deeper than 1800ft, with Fowey Consols being 2040ft from surface. A majority of mines had reached or passed the 1000ft mark but at least 80 mines were no deeper than 300ft, and many of these worked at or below adit level. If we were to include the scores of mines that had closed during the previous twenty years, many of them opening and closing several times until the Great War, we might find that a majority of 19th century Cornish mines were never deeper than 500ft. The same variety is seen in the extent of workings. Mines such as Carn Brea, Dolcoath and Clifford Amalgamated extended for a mile or more, whereas dozens worked a single lode for a hundred feet or so. Plans show that these small mines often had a couple of levels with a total distance driven measured in hundreds of feet. The great mines could measure their levels in miles, with some, such as Gwennap's United and Consolidated, totalling over 100 miles of levels. There was also a considerable difference in the size and value of the lodes worked.

Killifreth can be taken as a typical 19th century tin mine; it was a thousand feet deep, worked about four lodes, none especially rich, all relatively narrow, and produced insignificant 'burrows' of mine waste on the surface. It worked quite successfully for almost forty of the most difficult years in Cornish mining history. It never joined the top twenty tin producers but jogged along as an average mine of the second half of the 19th century. At its peak, in the 1890s it had 50" and 80" pumping engines, a 22" whim which also operated flat rods, and a 32" stamps engine. It also boasted one of the first 'safety cages' in a Cornish mine. Killifreth never employed more than 281 workers and only produced a fraction of the tin or copper of its great neighbours to the east and south, but it was more typical of Cornish mines of its day than any of these large and famous mines.

The switch of emphasis from copper to tin was a significant factor in the changes the industry underwent in the mid-19th century. Although tin had remained important during the revival of mining in the early 19th century, copper had continued to dominate the Cornish economy. By the 1850s many formerly important copper mines, especially in Gwennap, had long since closed. Production had been maintained, and even increased, by the discovery of new supplies, particularly in Illogan and areas to the east of Truro. However, copper lodes were being exhausted at a faster rate than fresh ones were discovered, and new, enormously rich discoveries of copper were being found in America and elsewhere. From the 1830s copper ore had begun pouring into Welsh smelters from across the Atlantic. It was not too long before the USA and Chile were smelting their own ore. Despite the peak in copper production the writing was on the wall for Cornish copper: the Williams family, who had gained fabulous wealth and power from the metal, whilst maintaining their grip on copper smelting were moving their money from copper mining into tin mining. During the second half of the century they became principal shareholders in Dolcoath, the largest tin producer in Cornish mining history.

In the central mining district of Camborne-Redruth-Illogan there had been a trend, as mines became deeper, to move from a copper zone of mineralisation to a tin zone. Charles Thomas, the manager of Dolcoath, faced with the imminent closure of what had been

ABOVE:
A PANORAMIC VIEW OF COOKS KITCHEN MINE AND DOLCOATH DRESSING FLOORS ON THE RED RIVER IN THE 1890S. DOLCOATH'S EASTERN VALLEY SHAFT IS BEING SUNK (TOP LEFT) AND A NEW ROUND BUDDLE INSTALLED BY THE RIVER.

perhaps the greatest 18th century copper mine, noted an increase in the quantity of tin ore in his deeper workings. This zone was met at a shallower depth in his eastern workings than in the west, but it was a consistent feature across the bottom of the mine. He persuaded the adventurers to sink deeper to check his theory that they were coming into valuable tin ore below the copper. They agreed, and very quickly Dolcoath Mine began to find unimagined wealth, this time from tin. Dolcoath Main Lode is one of the wonders of Cornish mining, extending for a mile east of the Great Crosscourse, being worked to depths up to 3000ft from surface and over 60ft wide in places. It has parallel branches that are 100ft across. This pattern, although not on the same scale, was repeated in the mines around Dolcoath and in other parts of Cornwall. Carn Brea, Cooks Kitchen, East Pool and South Wheal Crofty all found tin beneath the copper and went on to produce vast quantities of the white metal. Carn Brea and East Pool were at times close behind Dolcoath for tin production and, with other Cornish tin producers, soon began to replace revenue lost to Cornish adventurers by the collapse of the copper industry in about 1870.

Although tin was thus restored to its traditional position as the pre-eminent metal of Cornish mining, problems were far from over. Dolcoath, much as Wheal Vor in the first half of the century, dwarfed most tin mines but even her vast reserves could not entirely disguise the threat from increasing foreign competition. Since the 1820s, when Banca and Straits production had reversed the flow of tin from east to west, and the loss in the 1830s of the East India

BELOW:
BY THE 1880S, THE
CORNISH FOUNDRIES
WERE MARKETING
MINING MACHINERY
FOR SALE ELSEWHERE
IN THE WORLD.

Company's China trade monopoly, Cornish mines had had a survival battle. The price crash of the 'hungry forties' closed many tin mines and only the Dolcoath experience of discovering tin beneath copper lifted the spirits of mining adventurers. In the 1860s however, whilst Cornwall saw peak tin production, anarchy and piracy were plunging Malaya into chaos. By the beginning of the 1870s production in the great alluvial fields of the east was at a standstill. The price went through the roof, reaching a record £153 a ton, and tin mines opened, re-opened and expanded in all the tin parishes.

Just as suddenly it all went wrong. The Royal Navy intervened in Malaya to restore order and, inevitably, eastern production resumed and the price collapsed once again. By 1874 it was down to £56 a ton, and most of the re-opened mines closed. It bottomed in 1878 at an unbelievable £35 a ton. By that time discoveries of tin in Australia and Tasmania contributed to world production; ironically, it was Cornishmen who discovered it there and Cornishmen who rushed to exploit it. The next twenty years were among the most depressing in the long history of Cornish mining. In 1896 the price had dropped again to £64 and despair seemed to grip large parts of the industry. Amalgamations were the answer for many mines, just as they had been a century earlier when the copper mines had faced ruin through Anglesey ore. The Basset and Frances mines on the Great Flat Lode came together: Carn Brea, Tincroft and Cooks Kitchen combined; South Wheal Crofty acquired New Cooks Kitchen; and East Pool and Wheal Agar amalgamated. To some extent each group became more viable as the harsh winds of foreign competition, labour shortage and increasing costs threatened their existence.

ROCK DRILLS AND DYNAMITE

Whilst these traumas were producing great drama on the financial front, technology was advancing at an impressive pace. Steam was being harnessed to every conceivable process, and on the tin mines it was hoisting increasing tonnages up well-constructed vertical shafts. Cages and wire ropes were also being used to take the miners to their working levels. The surface plant was becoming more sophisticated as revolving Californian and Air-Cushion Stamps became widespread, as did Frue Vanners and shaking tables for ore concentration. All these improvements helped make Cornish tin mines more competitive. However, it was in mining itself where some of the most exciting improvements were made.

Since the introduction of gunpowder in the late 17th century all shotholes had been hand-drilled. Three men in an underhand stope could expect to drill two four foot holes in a shift. From the 1860s this situation began to change, when

F B Doering introduced a compressed-air rock boring machine into mining. Although his machine had only limited success, it was not long before others tried their hand, and another machine, the 'Barrow Rock Drill', was to prove highly successful. The 'Barrow' was patented by Cornishmen in Barrow-in-Furness, Lancashire, and was tried at Dolcoath in 1878. It was very efficient and advanced a level far faster than with 'hand labour'. It was made of gun metal, was reciprocating, and weighed 120lb. It was mounted on

BELOW:
MACHINE-MINER AND MATE AT PALMER SHAFT, SOUTH CROFTY, 1910. THEY ARE USING A NEW STEPHENS (CLIMAX) ROCK DRILL.

a 'bar-and-arm' and could be easily manoeuvred to drill holes at various angles. It worked well with air compressed to 50psi. Very quickly Cornish firms, notably RStephens & Son and

Holman Bros., became involved in modifying and patenting rock drilling machines, and they were soon joined by Tuckingmill and Sara's foundries. Some worked well and others fell by the wayside. Soon these 'drifters', some weighing up to 300lb, were being exported all over the mining world.

By the outbreak of the Great War in 1914, a great variety of drilling machines was available, including lightweight peg-leg stopers. Although machines were now equipped with a water line carrying water through the drill steel to the face, many working places, especially in small mines, still lacked piped water for such use. The resultant dust contributed to many premature deaths among miners. At that time most stoping in Cornwall was still done by 'hand labour', whilst driving levels and raising was by machine. Between the wars advances in rock drill design made them extremely efficient, and after the Second World War, drivage speeds and stoping tonnages increased considerably with improvement to air-pressure and the use of tungsten-carbide bits in the drill steels. By the end of the 1980s most stoping was by long-hole drilling rigs, which could drill holes with extended steels up to 30 yards in depth. Each 'ring' of holes blasted broke vast tonnages of ore.

Coincidental with the introduction of compressed-air rock drills was the invention of dynamite. From the 1870s this high explosive had proved effective, efficient and safe. One problem was that it cost far more to buy dynamite in Cornwall than in Germany or Sweden. Most mines in the county contributed cash to a fund to fight the 'dynamite patent', which was thought to be responsible for its high price. Eventually, as with gunpowder, factories were set up in Cornwall to produce dynamite. One of the most famous was The National Explosive Works on Upton Towans, near Hayle, and others were at Trago Mills and Herodsfoot, which were former gunpowder factories. By the 1930s use of black powder was a thing of the past and the fuzes made at the Bickford-Smith and Bennett factories at Tuckingmill were equipped with detonators for use with dynamite.

MINING SCHOOLS

There had been rudimentary schools for miners and mining students from the beginning of the nineteenth century. In the 1820s John Philips, a mine surveyor and assayer, set up a school in Tuckingmill, Camborne. Basic lessons on reading, writing, and arithmetic were supplemented by surveying, asseying and various mining techniques. Some students merely went to evening classes after work, but others attended by day and did full courses. More modern schools were first attempted in the 1850s, to train and improve technical education of miners in Cornwall. The Miners Association of Cornwall and Devon founded in 1863 aimed to give graduates certificates. In 1882 building began on the Camborne Science and Arts School which became Camborne Mining School in 1888. The principal was J J Berringer who taught asseying and William Thomas taught mining, ore dressing, and surveying. This was to become the world famous Camborne School of Mines. Practical lessons in mining and surveying began in 1897 at South Condurrow Mine centred on what is now King Edward Mine. Mining schools in Penzance, Redruth and Truro closed and mining students were concentrated at Camborne. During the 20th Century many thousands of mine managers, surveyors, mining engineers and mineral processors have been trained there and have managed mines on every continent. In the 1970s the school moved to Pool where it remained until, as part of Exeter University, it moved to Tremough in Penryn.

THE 20TH CENTURY: CRISIS AND SURVIVAL

For Cornish mining, the 20th century began, as had the 19th, quietly and then boomed. From a low of £64 a ton in 1896 the tin price rose to £181 in 1906, and mines recently closed immediately began to buzz again with activity. In St Just, Illogan, St Agnes, Camborne, Gwennap and several other old mining districts mines were re-opened. Some mines were fortunate enough to choose that auspicious time to modernise. Geevor was already being prepared for large-scale working, Botallack re-opened with modern plant, Wheal Jane went back into production, and South Crofty, reconstituted as a limited liability company, was brought up to date. Wheal Coates, North Crofty, Wheal Sisters and Phoenix had gained up-country investment and were going back into production. The creation of all this modern plant gained the period the epithet 'the electric boom'. The large amalgamations of the previous decade also moved ponderously forward and, among them, East Pool was to prove spectacularly successful. Its great variety of lodes, most within a short distance of its main shafts, proved extremely profitable. The discovery of Rogers Lode during the First World War was the icing on the cake, and was to prove one of the most significant discoveries in Cornish mining history.

Although there was a temporary slump after 1906, when the price went down to £133, by 1912 it was

back up again to a peak of £210, and another mini-boom occurred. Killifreth Mine, which had closed in 1897, purchased a second-hand 85" cylinder engine in 1912 to put into operation ambitious plans for reworking. Wheal Peevor, Droskyn & Ramoth, Wheal Hampton, Garlidna and Boswin all re-started, hoping to benefit from the rising price. It was all short-lived, for the Great War broke out in August 1914 and led to the near collapse of the Cornish tin industry. The price went down to £151, the best men went away to war, materials and gear were in short supply and mines such as Killifreth, Boscaswell, Condurrow, Wheals Jane, Coates, Vor and Peevor quickly closed. Even before the war several of Cornwall's largest mines were in trouble. Carn Brea closed most of its operation in 1913, Levant was beginning to struggle, and even Dolcoath was showing signs of wearing out. Dolcoath also lost more men to the armed services than she could afford and very soon men were being taken off development work to concentrate on production. This 'picking the eyes' out of the mine was eventually to be disastrous, for when the war was over no new tin ground had been uncovered for several years, the plant was unmaintained and in poor order, and there were no cash reserves to finance recovery.

Fewer than 20 mines survived the 1914-18 war, and several of these were in no condition to continue. The great Basset group of mines had closed, unable to cope with increasing costs and vast volumes of water. Dolcoath looked to South Roskear for its future, sinking a new 2000ft shaft there between 1923 and 1926. By the end of the 1920s the company was running out of cash, had found insufficient good grade ore, and failed to get extra backing. The 1930 tin crisis closed the operation finally, as it did most of the Cornish tin mines. East Pool also had its problems. In

1921 the two main shafts in its old workings collapsed, forcing the abandonment of a formerly rich area. It turned its attention to the new Taylors Shaft, on the north of the mine, and by the late 1920s this was the centre of all operations. It was equipped with a magnificent 90" pumping engine, originally built by Harveys for Highburrow East at Carn Brea. East Pool also focused on ground to the east of the mine, sinking Tolgus Shaft to 2000ft whilst driving the Tolgus Tunnel towards it at the 1600ft level. This ambitious scheme was no more successful than New Dolcoath had been.

The 1920s and 30s saw most of the remaining tin mines in Cornwall close, and even some persistent survivors such as Levant, Tresavean, Grenville and Tincroft had gone by 1930. Throughout the interwar years mines around St Austell, St Agnes, St Just, Wendron and Gwennap, and around the Tamar opened and closed. Some were tiny operations, with primitive plant, little cash and a handful of miners, whereas others were more sophisticated, well capitalised and on a larger scale. Polhigy in Wendron, Park an Chy in Gwennap and Wheal Kitty in St Agnes were all well organised affairs. The 1930 crisis closed all mines except East Pool. Even South Crofty and Geevor suspended for twelve months. East Pool's survival was not to last, for her ore reserves were meagre and by the end of the 1930s she was all but finished. Only government intervention during the 1939-45 war prevented the mine closing. At the end of hostilities support was withdrawn and East Pool closed.

The post-war years were extremely hard for Cornish mines, with both Geevor and South Crofty experiencing difficulty over recruiting skilled miners and raising capital. Both mines recruited Polish and Italian miners to make up for insufficient local labour, but despite good ore reserves and a tin price high enough to make mining economic, the two mines fell well behind in technology, machinery and modern mining methods. Carbide lamps for lighting, primitive tramming arrangements, narrow shafts, old-fashioned drilling machines and rocker shovels all gave the Cornish industry a dilapidated appearance.

During the 1960s all this was to change, as new investment, go-ahead management, a more ambitious attitude by the companies and an influx of keen young Cornishmen combined with a better tin price to create an environment for expansion and modernisation. For the first time since the war Cornishmen were enthusiastic about mining and were queuing up to work underground. By the end of the 1960s South Crofty and Geevor, the great survivors, were joined by a growing group of new mines. Wheal Jane, Mount Wellington, Wheal Pendarves, Cligga, Boscaswell Downs and others were being explored with a view to opening. Several went into production; some opened, closed and opened again, in the age-old Cornish pattern,

and one or two came to nothing. Wheal Jane Mine which worked for a couple of decades, although principally a tin mine, produced large quantities of zinc ore.

The tin price collapse of 1985 sealed the fate of Wheal Pendarves, Wheal Concord and other hoped-for revivals. Geevor closed in Spring 1986, re-opened for tramming twice in 1986 and 1987, and then re-opened for full production in January 1988.

Within months the hundred or so miners were breaking even, and with several stopes in operation and limited development the future looked brighter, but then the price collapsed again and after little more than two years Geevor was again on 'care and maintenance'. Wheal Jane closed in summer 1991.

The last decade of the 20th century saw Cornish mining in continuing crisis. The tin metal price again dropped and miners found themselves facing redundancy and the prospect of leaving the industry or going abroad to work.

In 1994, in a spirit of determined optimism, an important share flotation brought in several million pounds to South Crofty, much of it from local people keen to back the mine which had supported their families for so long. This led to Crew Natural Resources of Canada taking over the mine but, despite investing £6 million, significant achievements in opening up 445fm level and exposing and exploiting rich ore reserves, and despite the efficiency and skill of the miners, the sinking tin price meant there was little chance of profit or even breaking even. After over 300 years of almost continuous working Crofty closed on 6 March 1998. Within three years the mine was flooded to Deep Adit level and the future of Cornish mining looked bleak.

ABOVE:
ARSENIC CALCINERS IN THE 1920s. THESE FIVE CALCINERS WERE AN IMPORTANT PART OF CROFTY'S PLANT. ARSENIC ACCOUNTED FOR A SIGNIFICANT PROPORTION OF THE MINE'S PROFITS UNTIL THE 1940s, AND THE CALCINERS CONTINUED IN USE UNTIL WELL AFTER THE SECOND WORLD WAR.

RENEWED HOPE

Following the closure of South Crofty Mine in 1998 their assets were purchased by Baseresult Ltd, a private UK company, in September 2000. Baseresult invested £5M into the project and began the process of reopening the mine, but immediately faced opposition from Cornwall Council and the South West Regional Development Agency, both of which had other ideas for the redevelopment of the mine surface land, primarily as a leisure centre or 'hi-tech' business park.

Nevertheless, Baseresult undertook to renew the planning consents for the mine through a process called a Review of Mineral Planning, and fought the Development Agency to prevent a compulsory purchase order of the surface land being put in place. These actions culminated in new planning permissions being awarded in 2006. A Public Enquiry resulted in the Secretary of State concluding that South Croftys mineral resources are of strategic importance and should be safeguarded for the future.

During this period Baseresult actively sought a joint venture partner to assist with the financial burden of redeveloping and reopening the mine. In November 2007, shortly after the award of planning and the defeat of the Development Agency, a new partner in the form of Galena Special Situations Fund (a subsidiary of Trafigura) invested a further £5M in the project, sharing ownership 50/50 with Baseresult and Galena.

Baseresult began an underground development programme to drive a decline Westward beneath Camborne. About 31,000 metres of exploration drilling was completed between 2008 and 2013, and a new near surface mineral resource was Identified.

During the next few years a number of companies became financially involved with the mine and it's ownership moved between them. The Celeste Mining Corporation and Tinshield Inc and ultimately Strongbow Exploration were introduced to the project. This was finalised in 2016 when with the approval of Toronto Stock Exchange, Strongbow acquired Western United Mines Ltd (Baseresult), and the company was taken out of administration and became a wholly owned subsidiary of Strongbow. Strongbow immediately set about the task of bringing South Crofty back into production. The mineral permissions are valid for the mine until 2071.

Work began immediately to inspect and clear the main shaft and to clear the adit drainage system.

Strongbow's efforts in 2018 have been focused on advancing the dewatering of the mine. A water treatment plant has been designed by a team of engineers and the site preparation work completed. Equipment has been procured and it is hoped that construction of the plant will commence early 2019, with dewatering set to commence later in the year.

Importantly, as shown by a series of public meetings and meetings with local councillors, the local population is enthusiastically supporting the project. It is important that Cornwall Council have also shown their support for the project.

Meanwhile, throughout Cornwall, from Redmoor in the East to Breage in the West, new mining prospects have been investigated by a number of mining companies. This has included extensive diamond drilling which have had encouraging results. Over the border, in Devon, the large Wolfram deposits at Hemerdon has been exploited and there is hope for a long-term future there.

All this justifies the Cornish miners' optimism for the future of this ancient industry, which once again appears to have the prospect of a secure future.

BELOW:
A KIBBLE IS BEING TIPPED INTO A SMALL HALF-TON WAGON USING A HOLMAN COMPRESSED AIR WINCH ON 406FM LEVEL AT CHAPPLES SHAFT COOK'S KITCHEN 1893.

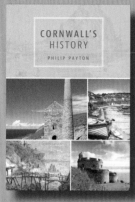

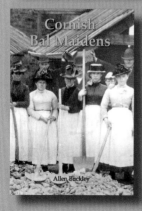
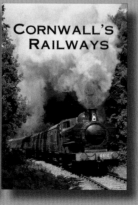